THE AMERICAN REVOLUTION AND THE BRITISH PRESS